SNOWBIRD

BOOK ONE*

WRITTEN BY
ERIN K WILSON

EDITORS:
ALISHA RAE
CASSIE GORDON
AMELIA BIRD

Fei,
Thank you!
-E!

*TRIGGER WARNING
THIS BOOK CONTAINS STRONG
LANGUAGE, THEMES OF
DEPRESSION & MENTAL HEALTH,
AND A BRIEF DEPICTION
OF SEXUAL ASSAULT.

THIS IS
A
GENUINE

erin
K
WILSON

GRAPHIC NOVEL

THIS BOOK EXISTS UNDER THE:

CREATIVE COMMONS 2013!

THIS MEANS YOU CAN USE STUFF I DRAW FOR OTHER STUFF
AS LONG AS, YOU KNOW, YOU AREN'T USING IT FOR TRYING TO GET RICH.
ALSO I'D LOVE IF YOU TOLD ME ABOUT IT SO I CAN LOOK AT IT.♡

SO THIS IS THE PAGE WITH ALL THE TINY TEXT
THAT ALL TALKS ABOUT PUBLISHING STUFF.
ALL THIS TEXT IS PROVIDED BY
(AND ALWAYS MENTIONS)
THE LIBRARY OF CONGRESS, U.S.A., EARTH.

IT IS DESIGNED TO MAKE BOOKS EASY TO CATALOGUE
IN LIBRARIES + BOOKSTORES

BUT THIS PROGRAM DOES NOT ACCEPT APPLICATIONS
FROM SELF PUBLISHED AUTHORS SUCH AS MYSELF.

SO, AS SOMEONE WHO WAS KIND OF GEEKED OUT ABOUT
THE WHOLE THING, I JUST HAVE TO SAY:

WHATEVER, LIBRARY OF CONGRESS!
I DIDN'T WANT YOUR TINY TEXT ANYWAYS.
I WAS ONLY PRETENDING.

ER IN
K
WILSON

→ ERROAR.COM
→ ERIN@ERROAR.COM
ERINKWILSON.TUMBLR.COM
SNOWBIRD COMIC.COM

BINARY SOLO → 01001100 01 001101 000011

WITH LOVE, TO:

ALISHA RAE

YOUR CONSTANT EMOTIONAL, MEDICAL, NUTRITIONAL, ⅋ POLITICAL SUPPORT HAS MADE WRITING THIS BOOK (AND MY LIFE) WONDERFUL, ⅋ MAGICAL.

≡ THANK YOU ≡

WITH RESPECT, TO:

JONATHAN HALL (FLEE)

JEFFREY GEERTS

JONATHAN GUERRERO

JUSTIN W LUTZ

MELISSA MARTINEZ

·NICOLE PACK (NIKKI)

KATIE SIMIANER

SAMUEL THOMPSON (SAMMY)

TONY ZALETA

(I REALLY HOPE Y'ALL WOULD HAVE LIKED THIS BOOK.)

CHAPTER
ONE

1

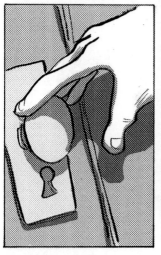

2

I grew up in Florida. I hated it as a child.

I wanted relief from the burning sun.

When I grew up and moved away, I missed that warm sunshine.

I began to realize how much I loved the gulf coast.

It's so beautiful...!

At age 23, I was finally proud to be from Florida.

Yeah, I guess you are right...!

It was MARCH, 2010 when I REALIZED that I was in LOVE with the Gulf

NOT EVEN one month LATER, EVERYTHING CHANGED.

The DeepWater Horizon spill was the worst oil spill in history.

ELEVEN LIVES LOST
AND
210 MILLION GALLONS RELEASED.

Without Hesitation, BP Began a massive "CLEAN-UP"

SHIT! I GUESS WE HAFTA DO SOMETHING.

DON'T WORRY, I KNOW A GUY.*

* RODNEY CHASE: DIRECTOR OF TESCO, MAKERS OF COREXIT. ALSO HE WORKED @ BP FOR 11 YEARS.

Two million Gallons of COREXIT was sprayed in the Gulf, despite debate between BP, the EPA, and activists.

YES, COREXIT HASN'T HAD ANY TOXICITY TESTS, BUT IT IS RATED "LOW-RISK FOR HUMANS" AND IS VERY EFFICIENT AT BREAKING UP OIL!

...I GUESS IT ISN'T ANY MORE TOXIC THAN OIL ITSELF.

WHAT?!!! NO!!! WE HAVE NO IDEA WHAT IT'LL DO WHEN MIXED WITH OIL AND OPEN WATER!

TWO YEARS LATER, STUDIES WOULD SHOW THAT THE ADDITION OF COREXIT MADE THE GULF'S WATERS 52 TIMES MORE TOXIC.*

* STUDY CONDUCTED BY THE GEORGIA INSTITUTE OF TECHNOLOGY AND UNIVERSIDAD AUTONOMA DE AGUASCALIENTES (MEXICO)

How can we help?

YOU CAN'T.

BP BP

People came from FAR and wide to volunteer their time and clean the beaches. But BP locked the coast DOWN so efficiently that NOBODY COULD even see it.

The People who did do the clean-up jobs were shrimping and fishing boat workers who were out of work. They had to sign waivers agreeing to never sue BP for any injury incurred on the job.

I SOLEMLY SWEAR NOT TO SUE YOU IF YOU ACCIDENTALLY KILL ME.

HAS NO OTHER CHOICE

Gooooood.

BP

CLEAN-UP WORKERS were NOT PROVIDED WITH RESPIRATORS BECAUSE THE EPA STATED THAT THEY WEREN'T NEEDED.

WITHIN A YEAR, SCORES OF CLEAN-UP WORKERS BEGAN TO SHOW SYMPTOMS OF TOXIC EXPOSURE: PARALYZING HEADACHES, AMNESIA, SEVERE GASTROINTESTINAL PROBLEMS, SKIN RASHES + LESIONS, BLURRING VISION, AND OTHER SYMPTOMS OF EXPOSURE TO NEUROTOXINS.

The explosion and subsequent spill began on April 20th. They capped the well on July 15th. Molly and I began our tour shortly after the leak was finally stopped.

Every day of our trip, I was painfully aware of our distance from the gulf.

I wanted to protest, scream, or find someone responsible and make them suffer.

Instead, I would spend anxious nights, reading every article I could find, trying to wade through BP's very effective media blackout.

Eventually, I would find myself engaged in my daily life, and forget about the spill.

But without warning, I would think of it, and waves of regret would unmoor me.

I had spent my whole life resenting the Gulf Coast and scheming to leave. Now, only mere months after my epiphany, the water was poisoned beyond reasoning. The timing was cruel.

I had always been alone. While kids my age were experimenting, I was reading comic books.

For years, I was the only virgin I knew.

I ended up losing my virginity to a sweet boy in Massachusetts when I turned 21.

It was the only experience I had where sex was a good thing.

For years afterwards, my experiences (few and far between) taught me that sex was a bad thing.

Eventually, I gave up on sex and spent my time and energy on making art.

This celibacy lasted two and a half years

14

It wasn't perfect. In fact, our dynamic was really unhealthy. We never honestly talked about our feelings, and that was equal parts my fear and his discomfort. I tried to hide how desperately I needed his attention. He tried to give me the attention he was not emotionally available for. He was interested in me casually, and i was madly in love with him.

In the end, the gulf between both of our feeble attempts swallowed us up.

By the time I realized he was gone, he had been gone for so long.

OH.

I had spent months in a one-sided relationship without ever knowing it.

Not only was it over ... it was becoming clear that it had never really started. I had been trying to live out a fantasy of "BEING IN LOVE".

I know, I'm so sorry. We are on our way.

My big secret was that more than anything, I desired intimacy. I needed it. What happens to you when you don't get something you need?

I considered myself a half-person.

GASP

My malnourishment was so normal to me that I had never noticed...

I lived with a shriveled-up heart.

Now that I had gotten used to being with somebody, the loneliness was bigger and deeper than before. Knowing what I had lost was so much more crushing. I was consumed.

...and we have to work together to stop this destruction.

So... Any questions?

thanks for your help. All we have to do now is load the truck...

I regretted the knowledge. I wanted my ignorance back. My lips felt burnt from the kisses I wanted to un-kiss. My body was seared with the touches I wanted to take back.

I felt that the air was full of poison.

I knew the water was full of oil, lead, or arsenic. I felt everything brimming with sickness.

I felt I was drowning at the bottom of the gulf, knowing it was oil in my lungs and feeling the panic of the whales, dolphins, and fish who did not understand why they could no longer breathe.

23

IN MAINE

I SKIPPED WINTER

If you don't have enough firewood you can go cold. You have to prepare months ahead of time or else you could be in trouble.

Not only does the temperature drop, but economic struggle comes into play.

Together, communities keep themselves warm enough to survive.

I'm SORRY... I JUST CAN'T STAY.

I was building community and trust in Maine... but I kept leaving.

I spent so much time preaching to audiences about fighting for land + community, yet I was torn between two *very* DISTANT communities.

they REALLY couldn't be farther away, could they?

My plans had been to stay in Maine, throwing off my Snowbird title.

SNOW IS SO WEIRD

But that plan was based on being with HIM

URK!!

This was no longer an option.

MOLLY.

...erin.

You are the only thing that has kept me together for the past three months. THANK YOU.

Later I would realize how miserable Molly had been. Taking care of me for months had been overwhelming and emotionally traumatizing.

But in pain, we are selfish. I had not taken the time to notice.

travel safe!

(I'M SORRY MOLLY)

In only three months I had completely unraveled. 90 days was all it took to nail the coffin on the Gulf. 90 days to make me wonder if I was too crazy and too ugly to be loved.

Perhaps we deserved to drown in the oil we spilt.

I was no longer sure.

29

I had four months until my next tour. Four months to try to pull myself together. Four months to find a good reason to keep going.

31

43

44

I LIVED exactly .9 miles away from the coffee shop.

IN THAT almost mile, I CROSSED ONE OF THE STARK RACIAL DIVIDES OF THE CITY.

I WORKED IN AN expensive NEIGHBORHOOD WHERE MOSTLY WHITE FOLKS LIVED.

I LIVED IN A POOR NEIGHBORHOOD WHERE MOSTLY BLACK FOLKS LIVED.

EXHIBIT "G"

ALRIGHT, CLASS. LETS TALK ABOUT GENTRIFICATION.

GENTRIFICATION

IS DEFINED AS THE CHANGES THAT RESULT WHEN WEALTHIER PEOPLE ("GENTRY") ACQUIRE OR RENT PROPERTY IN LOW INCOME AND WORKING CLASS COMMUNITIES. THE AVERAGE INCOME INCREASES AND AVERAGE FAMILY SIZE DECREASES. THIS RESULTS IN THE DISPLACEMENT OF THE POORER NATIVE RESIDENTS WHO ARE UNABLE TO PAY INCREASED RENT, HOUSE PRICES, AND PROPERTY TAXES.

HEY PROF, WHAT DOES THAT MEAN?

IN NEW ORLEANS, THIS OFTEN MEANS BLACK FOLKS ARE SYSTEMATICALLY FORCED OUT OF THEIR HOMES TO MAKE ROOM FOR PRIVILEGED WHITE FOLKS.

...

...AND THE TERM "PRIVILEGED WHITE FOLKS" MEANS ME

SHIT!!!

I HAD WATCHED FAMILIES MOVING OUT DUE TO RISING RENT IN JUST THE FEW YEARS I HAD BEEN WINTERING IN NEW ORLEANS.

MORE AND MORE WHITE PEOPLE MY AGE WERE MOVING IN.

BUT MY LIFESTYLE CHOICES MEANT THAT I COULD NOT AFFORD TO LIVE IN OTHER NEIGHBORHOODS.

I'M A FULL TIME ACTIVIST. BETWEEN TRYING TO SAVE THE WORLD AND WRITING COMICS ABOUT PEOPLE I HAVE ONE-SIDED CRUSHES ON... I JUST DON'T HAVE TIME FOR A JOB.

I KNEW THAT MY FRIENDS AND I WERE GOOD PEOPLE AND MEANT NO HARM.

BUT IT WAS THE PRESENCE OF KIDS LIKE US THAT LANDLORDS AND REAL ESTATE AGENTS SAW AS A SIGN THAT THINGS WERE "SAFER" AND THAT THEY SHOULD START BUYING PROPERTY AND RAISING RENT.

SWEET BANJO.

THANKS. I'M PLAYING LATER ON ROYAL.

I WAS WELL AWARE THAT I PLAYED A PART IN THE GENTRIFICATION OF NEW ORLEANS. BUT WHERE COULD I GO WHERE I WOULDN'T BE PARTICIPATING IN SYSTEMIC OPPRESSION?

SHOULD I GO BACK TO THE SUBURBS?

WHY DO WE STILL CELEBRATE COLUMBUS DAY?! HE'S SUCH A SCUMBAG!

RECCOMMENDED READING!

BUT THE SUBURBS ARE BUILT ON LAND THAT WAS STOLEN FROM NATIVE AMERICANS 500 YEARS AGO. OUR COUNTRY HAS A VERY LONG HISTORY OF GENOCIDE, OPPRESSION, AND RACISM. THERE IS NO PLACE I COULD GO WHERE THAT ISN'T TRUE.

IS THERE NO OTHER OPTION? ISN'T THERE ANY WAY FOR ME TO LIVE HERE AND BE RESPECTFUL?

YOU TELL ME.

LIKE MANY OTHER WHITE ARTISTS BEFORE ME, I MOVED IN DESPITE MY RESERVATIONS.

LIKE MOST FOLKS IN DOWNTOWN NEW ORLEANS, I LIVED IN A "SHOTGUN" STYLE HOUSE. (SEE OVER-HEAD FLOOR PLAN*)

IT IS CALLED A "SHOTGUN" BECAUSE IT IS A HOUSE WITH NO HALLWAYS. JUST A STRAIGHT SHOT... SORT OF LIKE LIVING IN THE BARREL OF A SHOTGUN.

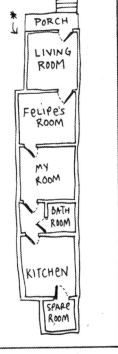

PORCH

LIVING ROOM

FELIPE'S ROOM

MY ROOM

BATH ROOM

KITCHEN

SPARE ROOM

APPROPRIATELY, THE INTERPERSONAL DYNAMICS INSIDE OF THESE SHOTGUNS CAN BECOME EXPLOSIVE. WITH NO WAY TO TRAVEL THROUGH THE HOUSE WITHOUT WALKING THROUGH A BEDROOM. PRIVACY IS IMPOSSIBLE.

LUCKY FOR ME, I AVOIDED THESE DYNAMICS BY HAVING A NOCTURNAL FIVE STAR CHEF FOR A ROOMATE.

GET A JOB, HIPPIE!

HE CAME HOME AT 8AM, RIGHT ABOUT WHEN I NEEDED TO WAKE UP FOR WORK

FIVE MORE MIN...!

I CAME HOME AT 4PM... RIGHT ABOUT THE TIME HE NEEDED TO WAKE UP AND GO TO WORK.

GOOD MORNING, SUNSHINE!

SHUT UP.

EVERY ONCE IN A WHILE
WE'D EAT OUR MUTUAL
BREAKFAST/DINNER TOGETHER
IN OUR EMPTY KITCHEN.

BUT MOST OF THE TIME...

...I WAS ALONE

KKRRRKIIIIKKkk

KKRRKK
KRRRIIKK
KRRKK

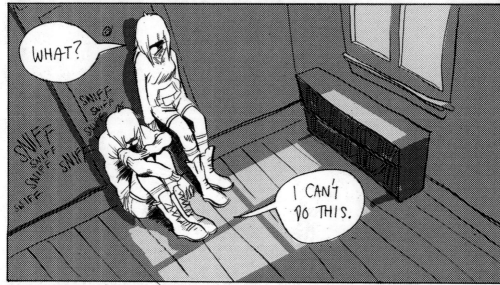

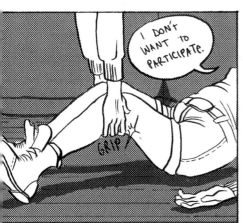

DO YOU UNDERSTAND THAT YOU'RE TALKING ABOUT SUICIDE?

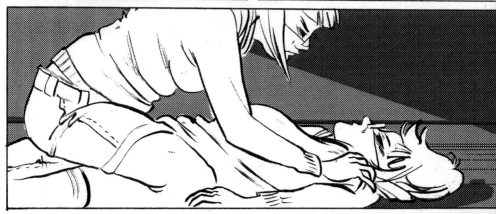

YES.

SLAP

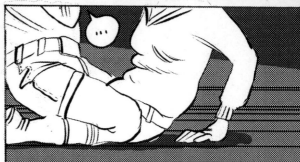

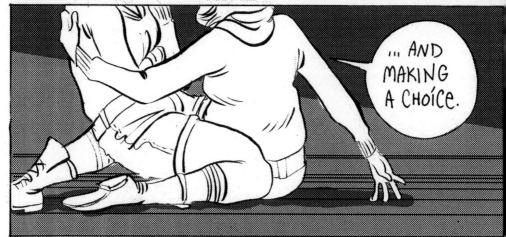

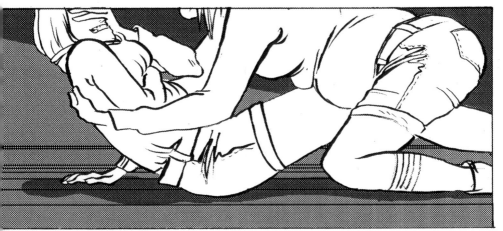

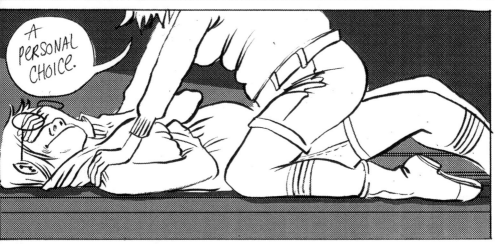

A PERSONAL CHOICE.

CAN'T WE JUST TRY?

PLEASE?

WE'LL NEVER FEEL BETTER IF WE DON'T WANT TO. IT'LL JUST BE A SELF-FUFFILLING PROPHECY OF "NEVER GETTING BETTER" AND IT'LL BE OUR OWN FAULT.

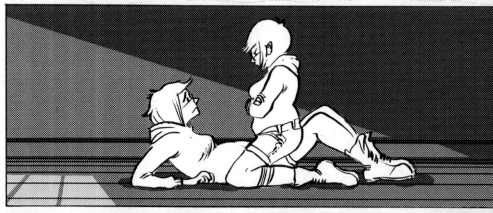

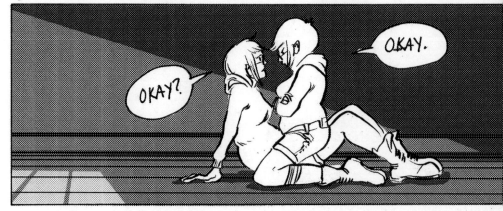

BYE

BYE...

ITS ONLY NOON...

IT IS WAY TOO EARLY TO GO BACK TO BED.

I KNOW.

YOU PROMISED TO TRY. WE HAVE TO GO DO SOMETHING BESIDES MOPE.

FINE.

-SIGH

WELCOME TO...

THE ARK

WAREHOUSE HOME TO...

I FORGOT HOW MUCH I LOVE IT HERE.

THE WHIRLY BONES ACROBAT COLLECTIVE

THE PLAN B COMMUNITY BIKE SHOP!

WILL YOU SHOW ME HOW TO CHANGE A FLAT?

WE CAN FIX THIS.

SURE!

HASBIN WILBY'S RECYCLED ART SUPPLY!

WHO THREW AWAY SPANDEX?

I FOUND THIS IN THA DUMPSTER!

NOT TO MENTION ALL OF THE ARTISTS WHO LIVED OR HAD STUDIO SPACE ON THE UPPER FLOORS.

BUT WHEN I WENT TO THE ARK, IT WAS USUALLY BECAUSE I WAS GOING TO...

WHERE HAVE YOU BEEN?!

I JUST GOT BACK FROM A TWO-MONTH TOUR WITH THE AAC. I LEAVE AGAIN FOR TOUR IN MARCH.

GIRL, YOU GET AROUND! DIDN'T YOU GO ON TOUR TWICE LAST YEAR?

YEAH... AND I TRAVELED TO MAINE AND HERE IN-BETWEEN.

TO BE HONEST, ITS KIND OF KILLING ME. I'M SO TIRED. THE ADVENTURE IS GREAT... BUT I HAVEN'T LIVED ANYWHERE LONGER THAN A FEW MONTHS IN AT LEAST THREE YEARS. I'M ACTUALLY PRETTY BUMMED THAT I'M ONLY HERE FOR **FOUR** MORE MONTHS.

ERIN, MARCH IS **THREE** MONTHS AWAY... NOT **FOUR**.

OH. SHIT.

SO... HOW LONG?

WHAT

HOW LONG IS "ONE GOOD TRY"? I WANT A DEADLINE.

TONIGHT 8PM.

FIVE YEARS.

WHAT! THAT IS TOO LONG!

FIVE YEARS IS A REAL TRY. THATS ENOUGH TIME TO HONESTLY IMAGINE THAT THINGS CAN GET BETTER. IT'S ALSO ENOUGH TIME THAT I'LL BELIEVE YOU WHEN YOU SAY THAT IT CAN'T. IT'LL BE ENOUGH TIME TO SAY GOODBYE TO WHAT YOU LOVE. GO TO THE MOUNTAINS. READ HARRY POTTER AGAIN. CAMP AT CAPE SAN BLAS. EAT SUGAR CAKE. GROW YOUR HAIR LONG.

...

OKAY.

SO, HOW LONG ARE YOU STAYING THIS TIME?

WELL, I LEAVE IN MARCH.

OH, WOW... THAT'S SOON...

I DON'T WANNA THINK ABOUT IT.

HOW WAS IT HERE THIS SUMMER?

OH, ERIN. YOU COULD SMELL OIL IN THE AIR SOMETIMES. EVERY-ONE WAS ANXIOUS AND ANGRY WITH NOTHING TO DO ABOUT IT.

HONESTLY, I WAS THINK-ING OF MAYBE LEAVING IF THE—

RING RING RING!!

SHIT!

RING!!

HUH...UNKNOWN CALLER. IT MIGHT BE ONE OF MY POSSIBLE TOUR VENUES... I'M SORRY, I GOTTA TAKE IT.

I'LL BE RIGHT BACK!

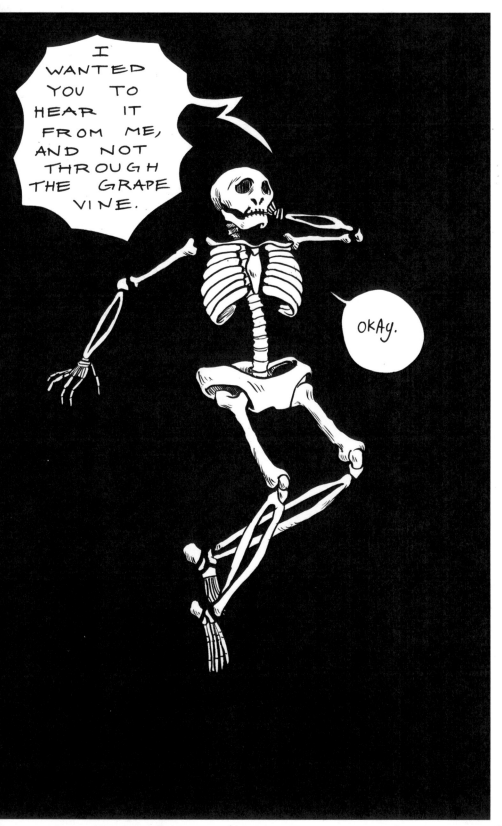

DNNnnn

≡HFF≡

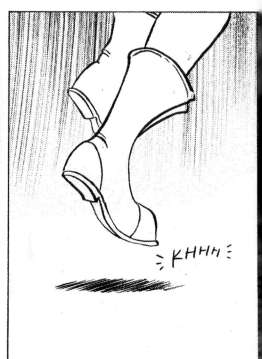

≡KHHH≡

There was a NARCISSISM IN my emotional UNRAVELING.

ERIN?

CRACK!!!

THE MAGNITUDE OF MY SELF-IMPORTANCE HUMBLES ME, even NOW.

ARE YOU OKAY?

≡CR-CRACK!!≡

I WASN'T READY TO FACE A TIME WHEN TRAGEDY PUTS YOUR EXISTENTIAL WHINING TO A SCREECHING HALT

AND YOU FEEL ASHAMED FOR TAKING THE TIME TO EXPLORE THOSE DOUBTS

BECAUSE THEY MEAN NOTHING IN COMPARISON.

CRACK

OF COURSE,
NO ONE IS
READY FOR
THAT.

END OF
BOOK
ONE

TO BE CONTINUED
IN BOOK TWO

A NOTE FROM THE AUTHOR:

HELLO THERE. THANK YOU FOR READING MY BOOK. IF YOU ARE ONE OF MY KICKSTARTER BACKERS, OR ONE OF THE MANY PEOPLE WHO LIVED IN NEW ORLEANS IN 2010, YOU MIGHT HAVE NOTICED THAT I HAVE NOT BREACHED THE SUBJECT OF WHAT HAPPENED THAT WINTER, AS I INTENDED WHEN I BEGAN.

FOR THOSE OF YOU WHO DON'T KNOW, SOME VERY TERRIBLE THINGS HAPPENED THAT WINTER. FRICTION BETWEEN ARTISTS/PUNKS/MUSICIANS AND THE POLICE INCREASED AND RESULTED IN THE SHUT-DOWN OF THE ARK (THE BUILDING CONTAINING THE IRON RAIL). SEVERAL PEOPLE WERE VICTIMS OF RAPE AND ASSAULT. THE ANNUAL ERIS MARDI GRAS PARADE TRANSFORMED INTO A RIOT, WHERE THE NOPD USED EXCESSIVE FORCE RESULTING IN 12 ARRESTS AND MULTIPLE INJURIES.

JOHN FLEE WAS MURDERED IN HIS HOME, AND ON THE NIGHT OF HIS FUNERAL 8 PEOPLE DIED IN A WAREHOUSE FIRE. THEIR NAMES ARE JEFFREY GEERTS, JONATHAN GUERRERO, JUSTIN W. LUTZ, MELISSA MARTINEZ, NICOLE PACK (NIKKI), KATIE SIMIANER, SAMUEL THOMPSON (SAMMY), & TONY ZALETA. I DID NOT KNOW THESE FOLKS PERSONALLY AND NOW WILL NEVER HAVE THE CHANCE.

IT BECAME CLEAR THAT I COULDN'T TELL MY STORY OF 2010 WELL WITHIN 100 PAGES. INSTEAD, I'M TAKING MY TIME TO WRITE THE ESTIMATED 200+ PAGE BOOK AND PUBLISHING THIS FIRST VOLUME TO FULFILL MY VERY LATE KICKSTARTER PROMISE. I'M GOING TO TAKE MY TIME TO BE CAREFUL AND INTENTIONAL WITH BOOK TWO - USING ALL OF THE LESSONS I LEARNED FROM WRITING BOOK ONE.

THANK YOU FOR YOUR PATIENCE, AND I PROMISE I WILL DO THE VERY BEST THAT I CAN. I HOPE THAT WITHIN THIS BOOK YOU WILL FIND SOMETHING THAT YOU CAN RELATE TO, AND THAT IT MIGHT ENCOURAGE YOU TO PROCESS ANY TRAUMA YOU MIGHT BE HOLDING.

-erin
(JUNE 2013)

LONESOME LEASH

ON PAGES 56-61 I FEATURE A MUSICIAN NAMED WALT MCCLEMENTS. HE PLAYS IN A LOT OF BANDS, BUT HERE I'M FEATURING HIS SOLO PROJECT, LONESOME LEASH.

IN THAT SCENE HE IS SINGING HIS ORIGINAL SONG "PELICAN" WHICH JUST SO HAPPENS TO BE MY FAVORITE SONG EVER.

LONESOMELEASH.COM

THE IRON RAIL

THE IRON RAIL IS A REAL PLACE! ALTHOUGH IT IS NO LONGER LOCATED AT THE ARK, IT'S STILL A WONDERFUL RESOURCE! YOU CAN VISIT THEM AT THEIR STOREFRONT AT 504 BARRACKS STREET IN THE FRENCH QUARTER OF NEW ORLEANS. OR YOU CAN VISIT THEIR WEBSITE!

IRONRAIL.ORG

RACISM

THIS BOOK CONTAINS MATERIAL REGARDING GENTRIFICATION, WHICH IS DIRECTLY RELATED TO RACISM. RACISM IS REAL. NOT ONLY IS IT REAL, BUT GENERALLY WHITE WESTERN CULTURE PRETENDS THAT IT ISN'T REAL, WHICH REALLY MAKES EVERYTHING A WHOLE LOT WORSE. IF THIS IS A NEW CONCEPT TO YOU, OR YOU ARE FEELING CONFUSED, I ENCOURAGE YOU TO EDUCATE YOURESLF ON THE MATTER. ONE OF THE BEST WAYS TO DO THAT IS TO ATTEND AN IN-PERSON ANTI-RACISM TRAINING.

I HIGHLY RECOMMEND THAT YOU VISIT

THE PEOPLE'S INSTITUTE FOR SURVIVAL AND BEYOND.

THEY ARE BASED IN NEW ORLEANS AND HOST TRAININGS THAT YOU CAN ATTEND LOCALLY AND NATIONALLY!

PISAB.ORG

INITIAL PAGES
BOOK TWO SNEAK PEEK

IN LATE 2011 I SAT DOWN AND WROTE THE FIVE
PAGES YOU ARE ABOUT TO READ.

THE IDEA TO WRITE A FULL LENGTH BOOK CAME
FROM THE DESIRE THAT I HAD TO TELL THE
STORY OF THESE NEXT FIVE PAGES.

I DIDN'T GET TO THIS PART YET, BUT IT WILL BE IN-
CLUDED (AND REDRAWN) IN BOOK TWO.

CONSIDER IT A PEEK AT WHAT IS YET TO COME, AS
WELL AS THE SEED THAT THIS BOOK GREW FROM.

ALSO IT'S PRETTY NEAT HOW FAR MY DRAWING
STYLE HAS DEVELOPED SINCE THESE PAGES.

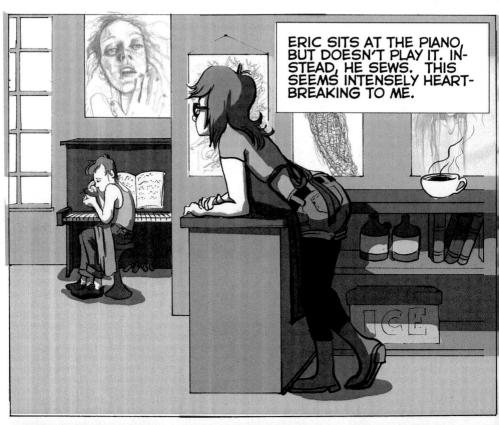

ERIC SITS AT THE PIANO, BUT DOESN'T PLAY IT. IN-STEAD, HE SEWS. THIS SEEMS INTENSELY HEART-BREAKING TO ME.

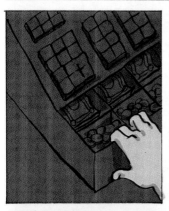
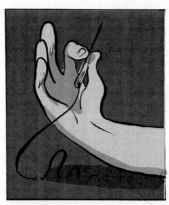

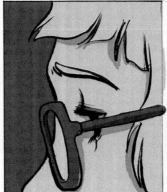
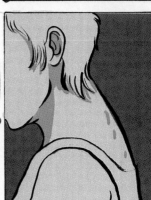

GRIEF NEVER LOOKS THE SAME.

I WAS NOT FEELING WHAT ERIC WAS FEELING... I HAD NOT KNOWN JOHN VERY WELL.

BUT I KNOW WHAT IT FEELS LIKE TO LOOSE SOMEONE.

WHEN TREY DIED, I WAS LIVING IN BROOKLYN. I HAD BEEN GROCERY SHOPPING WHEN I GOT THE CALL, AND I DROPPED THE BAG I WAS HOLDING. THE BOTTLE OF MAPLE SYRUP I BOUGHT BROKE AND POURED OUT ON THE SIDE-WALK.

I CRIED AND SCREAMED AND RUBBED MY HANDS IN THE GLASS AND SYRUP, LICKING IT OFF MYSELF.

I KNOW WHAT IT FEELS LIKE.

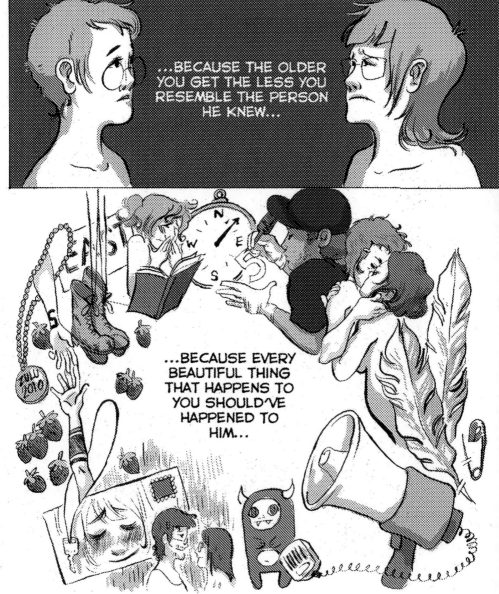

...BECAUSE YOU FORGOT WHAT HE LOOKS LIKE.

I KNOW EXACTLY HOW HE FEELS... BUT
THERE IS NOTHING I CAN DO TO HELP HIM.

WE CAN STAND SO CLOSE TO EACH OTHER
AND STILL BE FAR APART.

GUEST ARTISTS

THESE AMAZING ARTISTS PROVIDED ME WITH BEAUTIFUL ART-WORK TO POST ON SNOWBIRDCOMIC.COM WHILE I WAS OUT OF TOWN IN 2012! CHECK OUT THEIR STELLAR WORK!

NICOLE DEBARBER
NICOLEDEBARBER@GMAIL.COM

BEN PASSMORE
(MOST OF THIS BOOK WAS WRITTEN WHILE SHARING A STUDIO WITH BEN!)
DAYGLOAYHOLE.TUMBLR.COM

I want to run.

EMILJA FRANCES
EMILJAFRANCES.TUMBLR.COM

ALISHA RAE
I-AM-GOING-TO-BE-AWESOME.TUMBLR.COM

KICKSTARTER EDITOR'S BLOG INTERVIEW

Q: WHAT INSPIRED YOU TO TRANSFORM THE REAL LIFE EXPERIENCES YOU HAD IN NEW ORLEANS INTO COMIC FORM?

A: WHEN I WAS 19, I READ CRAIG THOMPSONS "BLANKETS". I HAD ALWAYS BEEN OBSESSED WITH COMIC BOOKS, MANGA, AND GRAPHIC NOVELS.... BUT I HAD NEVER READ ANYTHING LIKE THIS. I KNEW THEN THAT I WANTED, MORE THAN ANYTHING, TO WRITE THINGS AS BEAUTIFUL AS "BLANKETS". BUT I DIDN'T HAVE THE CONVICTION OR CONFIDENCE TO DRAW SOMETHING LIKE THAT.

... VERY SHORLY AFTER THIS AFTERNOON AT THE BOOKSTORE I HAD A TERRIBLE BICYCLE ACCIDENT THAT I WILL TELL YOU ABOUT SOME OTHER TIME.

I HAD SUFFERED A SEVERE CONCUSSION AND WAS UNABLE TO DO MANY THINGS... INCLUDING DRAWING.

**Q: WERE THERE ANY PARTICULAR EXPERIENCES THAT WERE DIFFI-
CULT TO TURN INTO COMIC BOOK PANELS? WHAT WAS IT LIKE WORK-
ING IT OUT?**

A: TO BE HONEST, THE MOST DIFFICULT THING ABOUT DRAWING THIS BOOK
HAS TO DO WITH THE ENTIRE CONCEPT. I SPENT A LOT OF TIME WORRYING
ABOUT WHETHER OR NOT IT WAS OKAY TO WRITE A COMIC ABOUT THE EVENTS
OF 2010. I WAS ONLY ABLE TO TELL MY EXPERIENCE OF THE EVENTS OF THAT
WINTER, BUT WHO WAS *I* TO SHARE MY VIEWPOINT? WOULD SHARING MY EXPERI-
ENCE BE HELPFUL AT ALL TO PEOPLE OTHER THAN MYSELF?? YOU KNOW, AS
MUCH EXISTENTIAL CRISIS THAT I COULD MANAGE.

**Q: DO YOUR FRIENDS EVER HAVE FUNNY REACTIONS TO SEEING
THEIR GRAPHIC NOVEL SELVES?**

A: THIS FUNNY THING HAPPENS WHERE IT'S REALLY OBVIOUS WHO
I'M IN LOVE WITH BASED ON HOW I DRAW THEM. YIKES!

KICKSTARTER COMICS

THIS BOOK WAS FUNDED BY THE CROWD-FUNDING WEBSITE CALLED KICKSTARTER.COM. HERE ARE COMICS AND DRAWINGS I MADE DURING/ABOUT THE CAMPAIGN

THE FINAL COUNTDOWN

ALISHA IS WORRIED

THANK YOU!

MOM, DAD, AND RICHIE FOR RAISING ME TO BE EXACTLY WHO I AM, **MY 368 KICKSTARTER BACKERS** INCLUDING THE INCREIDBLY SUPPORTIVE MARIKA MAYPOP, SUZANNE REICHARD, MALLORY MCMANAMON, SMITH POWELL, CASSIE GORDON, & TIMOTHY WALLS, **THE EDITORIAL STAFF AT KICKSTARTER** FOR HELPING ME BLOW THIS SHIT OUT OF THE WATER, **BREANNA** FOR BEING THE BEST FRIEND I'VE EVER HAD AND THE MOST HILARIOUS, INTELLIGENT, AND CARING PERSON I HAVE EVER MET, **ALISHA RAE** FOR BEING A CONSTANT INSPIRATION AND CONSPIRATOR, **LUCA MIRO** FOR PROVIDING DELICIOUS SHIT SANDWICHES MORE CONSISTENTLY AND HONESTLY THAN ANYONE ELSE, **AMELIA BIRD** FOR THE LIFE LESSON ABOUT COMMAS, **BEN PASSMORE** FOR UNDERSTANDING MY PHOTOSHOP INSIDE JOKES, **NICO KREBIL** FOR YEARS OF FRIENDSHIP & STUNNING VISUALS, **STAN STRINGSTON** FOR HELPING ME UNDERSTAND MY SHAME SHAME, **KATE HANRAHAN** FOR ALWAYS BEING THERE EVER SINCE DRAWING WITH CHALK ON THE SIDEWALK IN BUSHWICK, **DEVIN O. SARUS** FOR A BEING MY BABY MONKEY RIDING ON A PIG, **OWEN FELDBAUM** FOR THE VISITS IN MY BEAUTIFUL STUDIO, **KATHERINE WILSON** FOR PROVIDING ME WITH THE MOST INCREDIBLE AND HELPFUL CLASSROOM EXPERIENCE AN AUTHOR COULD ASK FOR, EVERYBODY AT **JUAN'S FLYING BURRITO** WHO TOOK A CHANCE ON A STRUGGLING ARTIST WITH NO RESTAURANT EXPERIENCE AND A SHORT ATTENTION SPAN, **NICK SUTTON BELL** FOR GETTING ME THE GIG AT THE FINAL HOUR, **JESS & LEE** FOR BEING MY FANS SINCE THE BEGINNING, **THE NEW ORLEANS COMMUNITY PRINT SHOP** FOR ENABLING ME TO DO ALL THE PRINTWORK I NEEDED FOR THIS CAMPAIGN, **JACKIE SUMELL** FOR INTRODUCING ME TO NEW ORLEANS IN THE FIRST PLACE, **KEHBEN** FOR CHALLENGING ME TO DO A REALLY GOOD JOB, **WALT MCCLEMENTS** FOR LETTING ME DRAW HIS LYRICS AND HIS LIKENESS, **HURRAY FOR THE RIFF RAFF** FOR PROVIDING MUSIC FOR THE KICKSTARTER VIDEO AND THE SOUNDTRACK FOR THE PAST 6 YEARS OF MY LIFE, AND I MUST BE FORGETTING SOMEONE. IF I FORGOT YOU, PLEASE KNOW THAT IT'S JUST BECAUSE I'M FORGETFUL. THANK YOU.